Mateo Fits In

by Scarlett Jones
illustrated by Christiane Beauregard

Harcourt
SCHOOL PUBLISHERS

Printed in China

ISBN 10: 0-15-350528-1
ISBN 13: 978-0-15-350528-7

Ordering Options
ISBN 10: 0-15-350334-3 (Grade 4 Below-Level Collection)
ISBN 13: 978-0-15-350334-4 (Grade 4 Below-Level Collection)
ISBN 10: 0-15-357520-4 (package of 5)
ISBN 13: 978-0-15-357520-4 (package of 5)

2 3 4 5 6 7 8 9 10 985 12 11 10 09 08 07

My first day in the fourth grade was the worst day of my life. It started last month when Dad got a new job in a new city. Before I knew it, we were packing up my stuff, and the movers came and put all our belongings in an enormous truck.

Leaving our home made me feel incredibly sad. I had to say good-bye to Ricky, my best friend. I remember waving good-bye as Dad drove away. I thought that was the worst day of my life, but I was totally wrong.

Now we live in a new town called Pleasant Gardens, but I'm really not sure why they call it that. Today is my first day at a new school, and I'm not too excited about that.

Mom woke me up incredibly early and made a big deal out of picking out a new outfit for me to wear. As soon as I put my new clothes on, my brother Hector came into my room and chuckled when he saw my outfit. That was how my first day in fourth grade began.

At the new school, I met my teacher, Mrs. Mott, who told me how happy she was to have me as her student. Then she chose a desk for me right in the front row. I wish Mrs. Mott had put me in the back because all the kids stared at me. During class, I could tell they were all staring at the back of my head.

Finally, it was time for lunch. All the kids snatched their lunches and charged out of the room, but nobody talked to me.

I picked up my lunch and headed to the lunchroom where I ended up sitting all by myself. I couldn't figure out where to get milk either. Lunch consisted of a squashed peanut butter sandwich, an apple, and no milk.

I thought for sure all the kids were talking about me, and I imagined they were discussing what a loser I was. They must have thought I had absolutely no friends. The lunchroom was an extremely lonely place that day.

Recess was even worse than lunch. I walked around the playground a lot, and I spent an incredible amount of time at the water fountain. I got on one of the swings because the swings are something you can do by yourself and not look too silly.

On the way back to class, some kid kind of pushed into me. This made me angry. I thought that if I let this happen on the first day, the kids would always pick on me, and so I had to do something.

"Hey, quit pushing!" I said quite loudly.

"Try and make me," the big kid growled right back at me.

"Where I come from, people don't push other people," I said, and I stared directly up at the big kid. It was pretty clear to me this kid was trouble waiting to happen.

The next thing I knew, a teacher was standing between us. "Mateo and William," he said, "would you two like to stay after school on the first day? I didn't think so. Now please get back to class!"

The rest of the day passed quickly. Still, no one tried to talk to me or make friends. Finally, the day ended, and I figured I'd just slip home without anyone seeing me.

I walked along the playground where some kids were playing kickball. I tried to sneak by, but suddenly, the ball flew right toward me, and I reached out and caught it. "Hey, good catch! Do you want to play?" one girl asked. I glanced around and, believe it or not, she was talking to *me*.

I put down my backpack and joined in the game. I was incredibly good at kicking the ball, not because I was good at sports, but mostly because I didn't want anyone to make fun of me. I ran around like crazy. Finally, a girl named Madison pitched the ball to me; I missed it and that was the end of the game. I didn't care.

After the game, none of the kids talked to me, except Madison. "Are you the new kid?" she asked curiously.

"Yes," I said, and since I couldn't think of anything else to say, I hurried to catch the late bus.

The bus ride home was almost as bad as lunch. I sat by myself again and tried to act prideful, but I really just felt terribly lonely.

The next day at school, I saw William walking toward me. "Oh, no, he intends to push me again," I thought but he just walked by. When I think about it, I recall he looked kind of sad.

At recess, I spent more time at the swings and water fountain. After school, the same kids were playing kickball. Madison called out, "Hey, Mateo, want to play?" I jumped for joy that this select group asked me to play with them two days in a row.

Suddenly, I noticed William standing there, looking kind of left out. I certainly knew how he felt.

"Hey, William, want to play?" I shouted.

William's face lit up, and he ran to join the game. He turned out to be the best player, practically kicking the ball right out of the schoolyard.

After the game, William and I wandered over to the late bus together.

"You're new here?" asked William.

"Yes," I said.

"Me, too," said William.

Now I understood that William was just as scared and lonely as I was. "Hey," I said, "want to sit with me at lunch tomorrow?"

William smiled and said, "Sure, that would be cool, and sorry about the whole pushing thing."

We talked about a lot of things as we walked to the bus, and then we sat together. It was like we had been friends forever. Suddenly, I no longer felt lonely, and I'm pretty sure William felt the same way.

That's the story of how William and I became best friends on the second day of the fourth grade. That day was one of the best days of my life.

Think Critically

1. What reasons does Mateo have for thinking his first day at school is the worst day of his life?

2. How does Mateo feel the first time the kids ask him to play kickball?

3. Do you think that William is a mean person? Explain why or why not.

4. Why is the setting so important to this story?

5. Why do you think the author wrote this story?

Social Studies

Neighborhood Map Pretend Mateo moved to your neighborhood. Draw a map of your neighborhood to help him. Be sure to include your school and other important places.

School-Home Connection Ask a family member what it is like to be the new person at a job or school. Talk about the story and compare your family member's first day in a new place to Mateo's first day at school.